THORA HIRD'S PRAISE BE!
CHRISTMAS BOOK

Elizabeth Gort has worked with Thora on *Praise Be!* for fifteen years, first as a BBC Television producer, and, for the past four years, as an independent writer and broadcaster.

The photo on the back cover shows Thora and Scotty with their daughter Jan.

By the same authors available as
Fount Paperbacks

THORA HIRD'S PRAISE BE! NOTEBOOK
THORA HIRD'S PRAISE BE! YEARBOOK

THORA HIRD'S

Praise Be!

CHRISTMAS BOOK

By Thora Hird
with Elizabeth Gort

Fount
An Imprint of HarperCollinsPublishers

Fount Paperbacks is an Imprint of
HarperCollins*Religious*
Part of HarperCollins*Publishers*
77–85 Fulham Palace Road, London W6 8JB

First published in Great Britain
in 1991 by Fount Paperbacks
3 5 7 9 10 8 6 4

A catalogue record for this book is
available from the British Library

ISBN 0 00 627590 7

Printed and bound in Great Britain by
HarperCollinsManufacturing Glasgow

Contents

Introduction

DECEMBER 1 St Luke – Gabriel to Zacharias – Slow me down prayer

DECEMBER 2 Advent Carol – St Matthew – Gabriel to Joseph – caring love

DECEMBER 3 St Mark – John the Baptist – Deserts – On Jordan's Bank

DECEMBER 4 St John – candles – Christingles

DECEMBER 5 Shopping for presents – country markets – the little mug – Cherry Tree Carol

DECEMBER 6 St Nicholas – children – gift of time – What is this life?

DECEMBER 7 Light Christmas pudding recipe – family cards – "egg custard!"

DECEMBER 8 Wrapping parcels – The Adventure of Timothy Church Mouse – All Things Bright and Beautiful

DECEMBER 9 Cards from old friends – good news, bad news – Simple Gifts – Jesus Christ the Apple Tree

DECEMBER 10 Journeys – walking to church – pilgrim's prayer

DECEMBER 11 *Songs of Praise* and *Praise Be!* at Christmas – O Little Town of Bethlehem – looking forward to *Praise Be!*

DECEMBER 12 Christmas cards – messages – Bless this House

DECEMBER 13 Mary and Martha – baking – recipe for rich Christmas cake

DECEMBER 14 Mary and Elisabeth – Christmas babies – Jan and Daisy – Evensong – Neville – Magnificat

DECEMBER 15 O Come, O Come, Emmanuel – Second coming – "I have overcome the world"

DECEMBER 16 The Holly and the Ivy – pagan carols – holly wreaths

DECEMBER 17 Time – London streets – crisis at Christmas – Ballad of the Homeless Christ

DECEMBER 18 War – loss of faith – hope – It Came Upon a Midnight Clear

DECEMBER 19 The Wind in the Willows – Carol singers and carol concerts

DECEMBER 20 Dickens – memories – John Betjeman poem

DECEMBER 21 Shortest day – death of the sun – pagans – birth of the son – G. K. Chesterton poem

DECEMBER 22 Christmas crib – fall of the sparrow – Eddi's Midnight Service (Kipling poem)

DECEMBER 23 Mrs Clarke (All Creatures Great and Small) – service of carols and lessons – the shepherds

DECEMBER 24 Dressing the tree with Daisy – King's College Chapel: Nine Lessons and Carols – Once in Royal David's City – tree at night – Silent Night – Midnight Mass

DECEMBER 25 Christmas mornings – Christians Awake! – going to church – Good Enough for Him

DECEMBER 26 Boxing Day Parade – Jan's Pumpkin Soup – letters – hospital – How Far Is It to Bethlehem?

JANUARY 6 The twelfth day – Isaiah – Epiphany

ACKNOWLEDGEMENTS

Introduction

Since I first started presenting *Praise Be!* in 1976 I must have received nearly a million letters from viewers, asking me to play their favourite hymns and carols. They tell me about themselves and their loved ones, their woes and joys, sharing with me poems, prayers and memories. So when I appear on television each year on *Praise Be!* I sometimes feel a bit like Santa Claus, coming into your homes with my sack of letters! Fortunately I don't have to come down your chimneys. . .

Do you know, I've always wished that we could have a special *Praise Be!* on Christmas Day. I'd love to be able to read out some of the wonderful stories about Christmas in your letters, and play the beautiful Christmas music that has been recorded over the past thirty years on *Songs of Praise*, most of which has never had the chance to be repeated.

When people ask, "Did you have a happy Christmas?" how often have you said, "Yes, thank you. Quiet . . . but that's how we like it"? Or even, "Yes, but I'm glad its over!" Christmas isn't always the happy time we remember from our childhood, especially for people who are alone. But it needn't be like that.

We haven't got our Christmas *Praise Be!* yet, but with the help of Elizabeth Gort, who is my friend and right-hand woman every year on *Praise Be!* and with a few suggestions from Scotty. I have been preparing this little book about Christmas. We've been looking around for things that aren't just made of tinsel or spray-on snow – coo! what a mess that makes, and what a job it is to clean it off again on Twelfth Night! – but I mean things which really make Christmas the wonderful, happy time that it is meant to be – whether you are one of a big family, or all on your own.

This isn't a book of ideas for presents, or of nostalgia for the "good old days", although we have discovered a few old customs you might like to revive. It's simply about ways of getting ready for Christmas to help us all wake up joyfully on Christmas morning.

The book is a bit like an Advent Calendar, and you can use it as one, if you like. Starting on December 1, read the ideas for each day of preparation for Christmas. Just for good measure, I've added a few of the important days after Christmas, ending with the feast of the Epiphany on January 6.

If you get this book after the beginning of December, don't worry! You might not be the only one to find yourself a little behind!

When we started preparing the book, war was raging in the Gulf, and for some families this Christmas is going to be a desperately sad time, whatever anyone says or writes. But I hope that these ordinary bits and pieces we've found, the stories, carols, hymns, songs, poems and prayers, will bring to all your Christmases the same message as the angels brought to the shepherds:

Don't be afraid. God is here. All is well.

December 1991   THORA HIRD

DECEMBER 1

Do you wake up on the first morning of December with a lurching heart? Oh, I do, and I keep saying to Scotty. "We'll never be ready in time!" Children feel happy and excited that it will soon be Christmas, but for many of us old 'uns it can be a time of pure panic!

> "I am Gabriel. I stand in the presence of God, and I have been sent to speak to you and to tell you this good news."
>
> Luke 1:9 (NIV)

It may not feel much like a message from an angel – that nasty jolt you get when you wake up in the morning to discover – eeeech! – it's December already; but you never know, it just might be. After all, you can comfort yourself with the thought that St Matthew and St Luke, when telling the gospel story of the first Christmas, both began with people panicking.

St Luke's gospel begins with old Zacharias being told by the angel Gabriel that he and his elderly wife Elisabeth (who was Mary's cousin) are to have a son, called John, who will prepare the people for the coming of a Saviour.

And Zacharias's story gives us the first step we can all take to get ready for Christmas, because when he showed signs of panic, the angel said to him:

"And now you will be silent and not able to speak until the day this happens, because you did not believe my words, which will come true at their proper time."

Luke 1:20

Well! I'm not suggesting that we all give up speaking for the whole of December! But if you feel the need to calm down, I've found just the prayer.

Slow me down, Lord!
    Ease the pounding of my heart by the quietening of my mind. Steady my hurried pace with a vision of the eternal reach of time. Give me the calmness of the everlasting hills. Break the tensions of my nerves and muscles with the soothing music of the singing streams. Help me to know the magical, restoring power of sleep.
    Teach me the art of taking minute vacations . . . of slowing down to look at a flower, to chat with a friend, to pat the dog, to read a few lines from a good book. Remind me each day of the fable of the hare and the tortoise, that I may know that the race is not always to the swift: that there is more to life than measuring its speed.
    Let me look upwards into the branches of the towering oak and know that it grew great and strong because it grew slowly and well.
    Slow me down, Lord, and inspire me to send my roots deep into the soil of life's enduring values that

I may grow towards the star of my greater destiny.
Amen.

From *Short Prayers for the Long Day*
by Giles and Melville Harcourt (Collins)

I like the bit about the "towering oak". We've got a
towering oak, over 300 years old, just by the church
door. I walk under its branches, and into church
through the south door, which is also made from an
oak, even more ancient than the living tree, and all my
day-to-day worries seem much smaller and less important.

We have so many very dear friends who live abroad that, though I say it myself, I've become very good about getting my cards for them written and posted in time – which in many cases means before the end of November. By December 2 it's already past the Post Office deadline for many places, but don't worry if you've not done yours yet. Send them off today – they'll arrive early in the New Year, and if you put in a loving message, no-one's going to mind. It's the love you send with them that counts.

And as an old Advent carol which I love says:

'Tis ill for a mind to anger inclined
To think of small injuries now;
If wrath be to seek, do not lend her thy cheek,
Nor let her inhabit thy brow.
Cross out of thy books malevolent looks,
Both beauty and youth's decay,
And wholly consort with mirth and with sport
To drive the cold winter away!

From "All Hail to the Days"
T. Durfey (1653–1723) (*Oxford Book of Carols*)

St Matthew begins *his* story of the nativity with Joseph's dismay when he discovers that the innocent young girl he is hoping to marry is already pregnant.

So the first Christmas sounds as though it began with scandal and disgrace. What a worrying time Christmas seems to be!

"This is stark stuff, Thora!" I can hear you say. "We thought you were going to give us some of our favourite carols, and poems, and Scotty's Christmas recipes!"

Oh, well, yes! And we'll be having plenty of those, all in good time. But we'll enjoy Christmas all the more for thinking about what it is we are celebrating.

So my suggestion for day two is that, instead of rushing around in ever decreasing circles, we all stop for a few moments and listen out for any angels who might be passing with a message for us.

"Joseph son of David, do not be afraid to take Mary home as your wife, because what is conceived in her is from the Holy Spirit. She will give birth to a son, and you are to give him the name Jesus, because he will save his people from their sins."

Matthew 1:20,21 (NIV)

The angel Gabriel, who told poor old Zacharias to keep silent, told Joseph not to be afraid to love and cherish Mary.

I don't think that buying our nearest and dearest expensive presents, breaking the bank and almost running ourselves into the ground, is at all the same thing as loving and cherishing someone who needs us. So today I'm going to take the time to find out if any of my family or friends or neighbours are in trouble and need my tender loving care.

As that old advent carol goes on:

This time of the year is spent in good cheer,
And neighbours together do meet,
To sit by the fire, with friendly desire,
Each other in love to greet.
Old grudges forgot are put in the pot,
All sorrows aside they lay;
The old and the young doth carol this song,
To drive the cold winter away.

From "All Hail to the Days"
T. Durfey (1653–1723) (*Oxford Book of Carols*)

And now I must write another batch of Christmas cards
. . . in fact, I'd better buy some more . . . and some
more stamps. Oh dear! Oh dear! Oh dear! I'll *never* be
ready in time!

DECEMBER 3

The beginning of the gospel about Jesus Christ, the Son of God.

It is written in Isaiah the prophet:

> I will send my messenger ahead of you,
> who will prepare your way –
> a voice of one calling in the desert,
> Prepare the way for the Lord,
> make straight paths for him.

Mark 1:1–3 (NIV)

St Mark's gospel doesn't tell the story about the birth of Jesus, but it does begin with another messenger. Not the angel Gabriel this time, but old Zacharias's son, now grown up and known as John the Baptist.

To hear John's message, people had to go out into the desert. But where are you and I going to find a desert these days? Well, not in London's Oxford Street, for a start! So on day three, we won't be going on a Christmas shopping spree.

Unfortunately, I experience being in the desert quite often. For me, it's when I wake up in the middle of the night, and I can't get back to sleep. I hear the church clock near us striking three, and then four and then five. My mind churns round and round. I can't very well wake up Scotty for a chat – it could be grounds for divorce!

I don't know what or where your desert is, but you

surely know one. It's wherever or whenever you feel, you know, a bit lonely and lost, and perhaps find yourself wishing that you had lived a better life. On the third day, you can use that experience to understand Christmas better. Find some time to be alone, and when you are, think of your desert and listen to the message of John the Baptist:

On Jordan's Bank

On Jordan's bank the Baptist's cry
Announces that the Lord is nigh;
Come then and hearken, for he brings
Glad tidings from the King of kings.

Then cleansed be every Christian breast,
And furnished for so great a guest!
Yea, let us each our hearts prepare
For Christ to come and enter there.

For thou art our salvation, Lord,
Our refuge and our great reward;
Without thy grace our souls must fade,
And wither like a flower decayed.

To heal the sick stretch out thine hand,
And bid the fallen sinner stand;
Shine forth, and let thy light restore
Earth's own true loveliness once more.

All praise, eternal Son, to thee
Whose advent sets thy people free,
Whom, with the Father, we adore,
And spirit blest, for evermore.

Charles Coffin (1676–1749)
tr. John Chandler (1807–76)

DECEMBER 4

The fourth gospel, St John's, starts:

> In the beginning was the Word, and the Word was
> with God, and the Word was God. He was with God
> in the beginning.
>   Through him all things were made; without him
> nothing was made that has been made. In him was
> life, and that life was the light of men. The light
> shines in the darkness, but the darkness has not
> understood it.
>
> St John 1:1–5 (NIV)

So what we'll do on day four is light a candle. Be careful
not to use a tall, thin one that might wobble and fall
over and cause a fire. One of those little night-lights
will do, or any candle that's short and round. Or you
might like to make a Christingle – and if you don't
know what that is, or even if you do, I'm going to tell
you anyway!

Well, to begin with, on the first Sunday of each month
in our church, we always have a Family Service, which
I always look forward to. (Being brought up a Methodist, I still find I get a bit muddled trying to find my way
through the Church of England prayer books. They
never do anything straightforward like going from page
one to page two! And no two services ever seem to

come from the same book. But the Family Service is short and simple, and we are all given a service sheet, so it's easy to follow what's going on.)

At the beginning of December, for the first Sunday in Advent, we have a Christingle Service: "an ancient Christian service from Moravia, revived in recent years by the Church of England Children's Society, in aid of their work for deprived children". (Well, you might know, I've just read that from the front of our service sheet!)

Every child under seven in our village, who has been baptized and is old enough to toddle, receives an invitation from Timothy Church Mouse – I'll tell you more about him another day.

During the service the children all come to the front and are each given an orange, which is the round world, tied round with a red ribbon, which represents the blood of Jesus, who died for the world. Then there are four cocktail sticks with sultanas and raisins sticking out of the orange, standing for all the fruits of the earth; and on top there is a lighted candle, to show that Jesus is the light of the world.

The children go round the church with their Christingles, while everyone sings an Advent carol. The singing is sometimes a bit shaky, because we are all holding our breath in case anyone sets fire to their own hair, or the hair of the child in front! You know the way little children carry things – very carefully held out just under their chins!

Ours is only a small village, but I'm here to tell you there were forty-one children in the procession last Christmas – I don't think, any of them could have been more than three or four – and the church was packed. A man who had not been to church for twenty years was there to see his grandchild. All the little girls were in their best dresses, and one two-year-old little girl, straight out of a Victorian Christmas card in her pretty frock, kept running to the front to look at all the candles and decorations. Nobody minded. There were some people there who usually only come to church for weddings and funerals, but you could see from their faces that they found it all very moving. And it was.

I only wished we could have had a film crew with us so I could have shown it all on *Praise Be!* When the hymn was over Roger, the non-stipendiary priest who looks after us in our church, said, "All blow!" and the children blew their candles out.

Afterwards there was orange juice or coffee and biscuits for all, and the children took their oranges home with them to eat! The collection was sent to the Church of England Children's Society.

You may have seen the *Songs of Praise* Christingle Service from Leighton Buzzard, where they sang the Christingle Song:

The Christingle Song

It's rounded like an orange,
This earth on which we stand
And we praise the God who holds it
In the hollow of his hand.

So, Father, we would thank you,
For all that you have done,
And for all that you have given us
Through the coming of your Son.

A candle burning brightly
Can cheer the darkest night,
And these candles tell how Jesus
Came to bring a dark world light.

The ribbon round the orange
Reminds us of the cost;
How the Shepherd, strong and gentle,
Gave his life to save the lost.

Four seasons with their harvest
Supply the food we need,
And the Spirit gives a harvest
That can make us rich indeed.

We come with our Christingles
To tell of Jesus' birth
And we praise the God who blessed us
By his coming to this earth.

Basil Bridge

I was going to make myself a Christingle, but the orange smelled so good, I've gone and eaten it, and all the nuts and raisins! But I've got a night-light, and now I'm lighting it.

So, Father, we would thank you,
For all that you have done,
And for all that you have given us
Through the coming of your Son.

DECEMBER 5

Well, there are only "16 shopping days left", as they say in the papers. I do hate the way they keep saying that, but a fat lot of difference that's going to make!

Have you noticed how some years the newspaper headlines all say things like: "ANOTHER RECORD YEAR IN THE HIGH STREET" followed by stories about how we are all spending so much money on Christmas presents, we're overheating the economy (don't ask me what that means). And other years it's: "CHRISTMAS BANKRUPTCY SHOCK FOR HIGH STREET SHOPS" followed by grave articles saying we aren't spending *enough* money on Christmas presents, and all the shopkeepers are going out of business. I'd like to know how much would be the right amount to spend, to keep our good names out of the papers!

Giving presents to people should be a happy thing, not something to be pressurized about. Scotty and I never give one another anything very expensive – in fact some years we don't give one another anything at all! We usually give Jan and the children rather bigger things. Last year we gave Jan one of those "sit up and beg" bicycles, with a basket on the front, which she'd been hinting at for a long time and had set her heart on. But what I really love best is looking for unusual gifts round the old markets when I'm in the north, or at village jumble sales when I'm in the south.

I was at a little country market last December, with my sister-in-law, Rita. We stopped by a stall where the man had some rather attractive little pieces of china, and a little pottery mug, bronze-coloured, caught my eye. I said to him, "How much is this?"

He looked up and said, "It's Thora, isn't it?"

I said, "Yes, it is, and I was wondering about this little mug – how much is it?"

He said, "Please, have it!"

"Well I don't want to have it," I said, "but I'd like to buy it if you don't mind."

Then he told me that his wife had died a few weeks before, and how he missed her. I said, "It's like having a big heavy brick lodged in your chest, isn't it?"

"Oh, yes," he said. "It is, and I'm that unhappy. I'll never get over it."

I told him, "The Lord gives you that heavy brick in you chest. Because you wouldn't want her to think you're not missing her, would you? But one day you'll notice that the ache has started to fade away a bit at the edges. It won't go all at once, and you won't even notice it going at first. But one day, you'll be left with only happy memories. You won't stop loving her, but that brick will have gone."

And I told him, "I've had one of those bricks – more than once. I still love my brother Nev, and my sister Olga, and my mother and father. But the bricks I had in my heart when they died, they've gone."

He just looked at me, and pressed the little mug into my hands and said, "Please have it. I'd like you to."

So now, whenever I look at his little gift, which has some yellow flowers in it today, I have another little word with "Him upstairs." Not that he needs reminding.

Cherry Tree Carol

As Joseph was a-walking, he heard an angel sing,
This night shall be born our heavenly King.
He neither shall be born in housen nor in hall,
Nor in the place of Paradise, but in an ox's stall.
Noel, Noel.

As Joseph was a-walking, he heard an angel sing,
This night shall be born our heavenly King.
He neither shall be clothed in purple nor in pall,
But all in fair linen as wear babies all.
Noel, Noel.

As Joseph was a-walking, he heard an angel sing,
This night shall be born our heavenly King.
He neither shall be rocked in silver nor in gold,
But in a wooden cradle that rocks on the mould.
Noel, Noel.

As Joseph was a-walking, he heard an angel sing,
This night shall be born our heavenly King.
He neither shall be christened in white wine nor in
red,
But in the fair spring water, as we were christened.
Noel, Noel.

Traditional

DECEMBER 6

December 6 is St Nicholas' Day. Or Santa Claus, as he is known – probably the best loved saint in Christendom! Did you know that he is a patron saint of Russia, sailors, and captives, as well as children? He lived in the 4th century, and his connection with children comes from a legend that he brought three children back to life who had been pickled in a brine-tub.

If you see a picture of him in Russian art, he's in the gorgeous robes of a bishop, the three children in a tub are at his feet, or he has three golden balls on a book, or sometimes it's three money bags. He is often shown with a ship, or an anchor, or calming a storm.

Which is all a long chalk from being a jolly, fat man with a snowy white beard and red costume! Or a man who comes down the chimney carrying a sack full of presents, and drives across the sky in a sleigh pulled by reindeer. . . Never mind. On Santa Claus's special day, let's do something to help bring back to life any children we know, pickled in a brine-tub of television and videos!

If you haven't got children or grandchildren of your own, you'll be a godsend to a harassed mother if you offer to take a friend's or neighbour's children off to see a pantomine, or invite them round and play cards or board games with them. Or take them for a walk, and tell them a story.

You could even offer them the chance to earn some Christmas pocket money by giving them jobs to do in your garden, or washing the car, or getting your shopping. And when they've done the work, invite them in for a cup of tea or a cola. Bake them a cake! Well, why not? Children have a lot of time on their hands in the holidays, and for many of them their biggest problem is knowing what to do with themselves. The best thing you can give them is your time.

Leisure

What is this life if, full of care,
We have no time to stand and stare.

No time to stand beneath the boughs
And stare as long as sheep or cows.

No time to see, when woods we pass,
Where squirrels hide their nuts in grass.

No time to see, in broad daylight,
Streams full of stars, like skies at night.

No time to turn at Beauty's glance,
And watch her feet, how they can dance.

No time to wait till her mouth can
Enrich that smile her eyes began.

A poor life this if, full of care,
We have no time to stand and stare.

W. H. Davies (1871–1940)

DECEMBER 7

We could make our Christmas pudding today, but Scotty is the family cook, and he's always made our pudding way back in November. Still, you might not have made yours yet, so I thought I'd give you a special recipe which is delicious, and it doesn't need to be made weeks in advance. It's much lighter than the normal Christmas pud, higher in fibre, and lower in sugar and fat, so it's not so filling if you're eating it after a big helping of turkey or goose!

Light Christmas Pudding Recipe

8oz/230g fresh wholemeal breadcrumbs
8oz roughly chopped muscatel raisins
8oz roughly chopped sultanas
8oz roughly chopped dried apricots
4oz/110g chopped stoned prunes
2oz/60g crumbled almond macaroons
2oz chopped almonds
1oz/30g ground or flaked almonds
1 peeled and grated apple
1 tbsp ground cinnamon
1 tsp ground mace
½ tsp ground cardamom
½ tsp ground cloves
½ tsp ground allspice

2 tbsp orange marmalade (or candied orange peel)
juice of 1 small orange
4 size 3 eggs
1 miniature bottle brandy or orange liqueur
¼pt/140ml fortified muscat wine, port, or Marsala.

And this is what you do:

Put all the dry ingredients in a large bowl, and mix with a large wooden spoon.

Put the marmalade, orange juice, eggs, brandy and wine in another large bowl, or in a blender, and beat well until frothy.

Pour this liquid over the dry ingredients.

Mix again until all the mixture is moist.

Cover, and let it stand for a couple of hours or longer (overnight if possible).

Grease the pudding basin or basins (the mixture fills a 3-pint basin) and spoon in the mixture. (You can fill to within ½ inch of the rim, because it won't expand very much during cooking.)

Take a large square of greaseproof paper, grease it, pleat it and tie it over the top of the pudding basin with string.

Place the basin on a heatproof upturned saucer or dish in a saucepan, standing it on a long triple strip of foil to help you lift the hot basin out of the saucepan once cooked.

Pour in boiling water to reach halfway up the pudding basin, cover the saucepan, and bring it back to the boil.

Lower the heat, keep water at a steady simmer, and steam the pudding for five to six hours.

(Make sure the water is kept topped up and boiling.)

When the pudding is cooked, allow it go completely cold before wrapping in fresh greaseproof paper and foil.

When you want to serve it, steam for a further two hours.

Mmm. I might even make one myself!

Another thing I'll do today is write some verses to put into each of the family's Christmas cards. You couldn't call what I write poetry, it's just doggerel, but I think they like it.

One day when Daisy was little, Jan was trying to get her to finish her lunch and she was being naughty. I came in and saw that it was egg custard in her bowl, and I said enthusiastically, "Ooooh! *Egg custard*!" and for some reason this gave her the giggles, and it has remained a running joke between Daisy and me ever since. The game now is to try to get "egg custard" into any letter or card we send one another, but the rule is that you always have to find a different rhyme for it – you know, words like mustard and flustered and blustered. As the years go by, this is becoming more and more difficult, but I think I've thought of a good one for this Christmas:

> Computers make me cross and foxed
> And videos are just 'ard
> but when you open up this box –
> It's easy as *Egg Custard*!

DECEMBER 8

While you're wrapping up any little gifts you may be sending by post, I'll tell you the story that Roger, our non-stipendiary priest, told the children at the Christingle Service one year. (Yes, I thought you might ask me that. I think "non-stipendiary" just means he doesn't get paid!)

Roger always tells us the latest adventures of Timothy Church Mouse, who lives at No 1 Flat, The Organ, St Margaret's. And this was the story of how Timothy arranged for our village organist, Malcolm Cleroux, to play for Evensong in Chichester Cathedral. And I shall tell you the story in Roger's own words – so you must imagine a lovely deep, West Country drawl as well.

The Adventures of
Timothy Church Mouse

Timothy went to visit his cousin Cyril, a very self-important mouse, who lived at The Cathedral Organ, Chichester. Anyway, it was Cyril's birthday, so they had a meal at Letitia Lamb's Tea Shop, of bangers and mash. And jelly. And um – orangeade.

And then after tea, Cyril showed Timothy round his place. And Timothy was naturally quite overwhelmed, because the Cathedral was so big. And Cyril said, "And this is my house", leading him up to the biggest organ Timothy had ever seen, and this was called, um – "*Electronic Transistor*".

And Cyril said, "What's your organ called?"

Timothy was quite embarrassed, so he said quickly, "Oh, I believe it's called, er, Malcolm."

Cyril said, "Electronic Transistor is a Miracle of Modern Technology."

Well, Timothy hadn't got a *clue* what that meant. But he thought it was impressive.

Anyway, the procession was just coming in, and Cyril told Timothy who all these important people were – the Bishop, the Dean, the Archdeacon, the Residentiary Canons, the altar servers and a huge choir. The service started with a hymn, and Timothy looked at his sheet but he couldn't understand a word of it. Cyril whispered, "*Latin!*"

But when the first note began there was a loud "BANG!" from Electronic Transistor – a big blue spark came out, and the organist fell off his seat.

Now, as luck would have it, Timothy had brought along with him a cassette-recording of his organ, Malcolm, which was his birthday present for Cyril. And Cyril was going to record the Cathedral service anyway, so they put the cassette into his machine and switched it on, and the two mice held it up to the microphone and a voice said, "The first hymn will be 'All things Bright and Beautiful'."

The Dean looked a bit surprised, but the congregation put down their service sheets and picked up their hymn books, and found the number. And then, every time there was a hymn, the Dean simply nodded to Timothy, and he pressed the starter on the cassette recorder.

So it went quite well, and afterwards Timothy and

Cyril were invited round to the Bishop's Palace, and everybody shook Timothy by the paw most warmly, and congratulated him on how he and "Malcolm" had come to the rescue.

Then, unfortunately, the organ repair-man worked out what had happened. He appeared at the Bishop's Palace and he said, " 'Ere, Bishop, what joker left this cheese sandwich inside Electronic Transistor, on his main circuit board?"

Cyril went crimson to the roots of his whiskers!

The Bishop's wife rushed over with a cucumber sandwich to help smooth over the situation, and Timothy said, "Cyril, I must be going home now", so Cyril walked with him to the station. They didn't talk much, and when Timothy's train came in, they shook paws, and Cyril just said, "Thank you, Timothy, you've been an absolute brick."

And I have heard that Cyril's been a nicer mouse ever since!

Now, all you organ buffs, don't write and tell me I've got it all wrong. "Electronic Transistor" was a faithful servant of the Cathedral for more than 10 years, and now he's retired and they've got a lovely pipe organ, called Alan. Last time I was in there someone who looked remarkably like Timothy's cousin Cyril pointed up to the arches above the nave, where it seems Electronic Transistor slumbers until he's needed again.

All Things Bright and Beautiful

All things bright and beautiful,
All creatures great and small,
All things wise and wonderful, –
The Lord God made them all.

Each little flower that opens,
Each little bird that sings, –
He made their glowing colours,
He made their tiny wings.

The purple-headed mountain,
The river running by,
The sunset and the morning
That brightens up the sky,

The cold wind in the winter,
The pleasant summer sun,
The ripe fruits in the garden, –
He made them every one.

The tall trees in the greenwood,
The meadows where we play,
The rushes by the water,
We gather every day, –

He gave us eyes to see them,
And lips that we might tell
How great is God Almighty,
Who has made all things well.

All things bright and beautiful,
All creatures great and small,
All things wise and wonderful, –
The Lord God made them all.

Mrs Cecil Frances Alexander 1818–95

DECEMBER 9

The postman brings us a pile of Christmas cards every morning now. Of course I always look out for the Morecambe postmark on the envelopes. We only hear from some of our old friends once a year now, at Christmas, where once we saw them every day, when we were neighbours. Oh! Their cards do bring back wonderful memories of happy days.

Scotty and I always stop for a cup of coffee midmorning, and we have a natter about all the people we've heard from that day. I remember people best when I'm telling stories of incidents that happened when we were with them. As I talk, I can see the person, just as if they were back in the room with us.

We take the cards down to the cottage. I cover each of the long walls in the passage with seven lines of coloured string, about ten inches apart, and then hang the cards along the strings. I think they look nice like that, and they don't keep falling down.

Sometimes it's from Christmas cards that we hear for the first time that an old friend has been ill in the past year, or gone into hospital or a nursing home. It's then, in the middle of winter, that we suddenly find ourselves having to take stock of things, ourselves and our friends getting older and dying. But this, too, is a rite of passage, and part of our journey towards Christmas.

The American Shaker sect in the last century had this beautiful little song in their hymnal:

Simple Gifts

'Tis the gift to be simple, 'tis the gift to be free,
'Tis the gift to come down where you ought to be,
And when we find ourselves in the place just right,
'Twill be in the valley of love and delight.

When true simplicity is gained,
To bow and to bend we shan't be ashamed;
To turn, turn will be our delight,
Till by turning, turning we come round right.

Song of the Shaker sect (American, 1837–47)

Another beautiful American song sometimes sung by church choirs at this time of year is 'Jesus Christ the Apple Tree', and if you are feeling at all down-hearted or weary at this time of year, to read these words or hear them sung, will be a real tonic:

Jesus Christ the Apple Tree

The tree of life my soul hath seen,
Laden with fruit and always green.
The trees of nature fruitless be
Compared with Christ the apple tree

His beauty doth all things excel;
By faith I know, but ne'er can tell

The glory which I now can see
In Jesus Christ the apple tree.

For happiness I long have sought,
And pleasure dearly I have bought.
I missed of all; but now I see
'Tis found in Christ the apple tree.

I'm weary with my former toil,
Here I will sit and rest awhile:
Under the shadow I will be,
Of Jesus Christ the apple tree.

This fruit doth make my soul to thrive,
It keeps my dying faith alive;
Which makes my soul in haste to be
With Jesus Christ the apple tree.

Anon (Collection of Joshua Smith,
New Hampshire, 1784)

DECEMBER 10

There's a lot about journeys in the gospel Christmas stories. Mary and Joseph, like thousands of other families at that time, because of the Roman census, travelling with their little donkey from Nazareth to Bethlehem; the shepherds coming in from the hill country to find the new-born baby; the three wise men following the star in the east. Then later, Joseph and Mary escaping with their baby from the danger of being found and killed by King Herod, slipping away into hiding in Egypt.

A lot of people still travel at Christmas time. Some people go abroad, often to where there are mountains so they can ski, and forget about family Christmases altogether. Others make it a time for family gatherings – and that's what I choose. And while we are all together, we make little journeys. One of my favourite walks is to go with Jan and the dogs along the path that leads to our church, which is in quite an isolated spot, at the end of a lovely country lane. The River Ouse (I mean the Sussex Ouse, of course) runs close by the church, and you can still see signs of locks from when it was a busy thoroughfare for barges. They're all derelict now from disuse. You can also see the earthworks of a medieval wooden fortress guarding a ford in the river. And there was once a Roman road just to the west, running due north all the way from Newhaven to London.

So once our little church was at the centre of all the

main thoroughfares, not hidden away at the end of a little country path. Some people might think that this reflects its decline in importance in the modern world. And I think just the opposite! I think it's a sign of how great and timeless God's love is. The great Roman and Victorian empires have grown up and faded away around our little church. But it's still there.

Like the river beside it, the church sometimes over-flows with people and energy and ideas, and sometimes there's only a small trickle. But it's always here, and I reckon that in a thousand years' time it will still be here. It might have changed shape a few times, but it'll still be here.

There's a prayer I like, printed at the back of our little Church Guide:

May your pilgrimage here give you fresh inspiration
for life's pilgrimage.
May you have an increased sense of wonder at the
natural beauty of this part of Sussex, in which this
village church is so superbly set.
May you have an increased sense of appreciation of
the artistic skill, and religious faith, of our
forefathers.
May you have an increased sense of gratitude to God
for all his many gifts.
And may you have a safe journey home.

DECEMBER 11

Although *Praise Be!* always goes out in the Spring, I play hymns from the whole of the past year of *Songs of Praise*, including the Advent and Christmas programmes – where we often hear some of the loveliest music and singing. Do you remember the programme from the village of Clare one year, with a sprinkling of snow on the ground outside, and John Rutter and his choir from Clare College, Cambridge, leading the singing by candlelight in the old village church? That was beautiful. Or the programme from Warwick Castle, with the donkey and the baby? And did you see *Songs of Praise* in 1990 (after we'd been through a year of so many dramatic changes in Eastern Europe, including the dismantling of the Berlin Wall) when it came from Prague, with Placido Domingo?

Some people complain when I include Christmas carols in my spring or early summer series of *Praise Be!* but I always like to remind everyone of some of the high spots, and of course, lots of you write especially asking me to, so I expect I shall carry on regardless!

The carol which always gets most requested is one which almost makes you feel that Christmas is happening for the first time here and now, and in your own home town:

O Little Town of Bethlehem

O little town of Bethlehem,
How still we see thee lie!
Above thy deep and dreamless sleep
The silent stars go by
Yet in thy dark streets shineth
The everlasting Light;
The hopes and fears of all the years
Are met in thee to-night.

O morning stars, together
Proclaim the holy birth
And praises sing to God the King,
And peace to men on earth.
For Christ is born of Mary;
And, gathered all above,
While mortals sleep, the angels keep
Their watch of wond'ring love.

How silently, how silently,
The wondrous gift is given!
So God imparts to human hearts
The blessings of His heaven.
No ear may hear His coming;
But in this world of sin,
Where meek souls will receive Him, still
The dear Christ enters in.

Where children pure and happy
Pray to the blessed child,
Where misery cries out to thee,
Son of the mother mild;
Where charity stands watching
And faith holds wide the door,

The dark night wakes, the glory breaks,
And Christmas comes once more.

O Holy Child of Bethlehem,
Descend to us, we pray;
Cast out our sin, and enter in,
Be born in us to-day.
We hear the Christmas angels
The great glad tidings tell:
O come to us, abide with us,
Our Lord Emmanuel.

Bishop Phillips Brooks (1835–93)

The days are still getting shorter and I must remember to put light bulbs on the shopping list. It gets dark so early, and if you're like us, you're forever replacing them at this time of year, and running out.

Let's use this dark day to be hopeful, looking forward to spring sunshine and new friendships, and the days when we shall all be together again on *Praise Be!* You might even write me a letter!

DECEMBER 12

I love looking at all the different kinds of Christmas cards, don't you? They probably say a lot about us, the cards we choose!

One very popular sort are reproductions of eighteenth-century scenes – stagecoaches with teams of horses driving through a winter landscape, or at a crossroads with thigh-booted men holding up lanterns, and ladies in long, hooded cloaks. And fine mansion houses with bright light streaming from bow windows, where inside they are dispensing brandy-tinted hospitality to guests in gorgeous clothes. And hunting dogs stretch out in front of crackling log fires. I don't think many of our friends live in quite such grand establishments – but they can dream, can't they? (Although I've never quite seen what it all has to do with the birth of a baby in Bethlehem!)

And I love Victorian Christmas cards, don't you, of enormous decorated Christmas trees, with heaps of coloured presents below, and children dancing round.

We always get lots of different snow-scenes. Usually with a robin. The robin's haunting winter song, when other birds are silent or have flown away, and that legend – do you know it? – of how he got his red breast through helping Jesus on the Cross by trying to remove the cruel thorns from his crown. . . I hope it's true, and I think that's why he appears on so many cards and Advent Calendars.

Santa Claus is an even more popular figure, particularly on humorous cards, often wedged tight down someone's chimney, while some mischievous person lights a fire in the grate underneath him!

Then there are always pictures of the nativity scene, with Mary and Joseph, Jesus in his manger, angels in the sky above, while shepherds, ox and ass look on. And the three wise men with their gifts visit us again and again. Among my favourites are the ones where people have made a recent family photograph into their Christmas card. If they do it every year, you can see all sorts of changes as time goes by – children grow up, different dogs and cats come and go, the arrival of grandchildren.

However interesting the pictures on Christmas cards might be, the ones which mean far the most are the ones where friends have taken the time to write more than just their names inside, and have put a little personal message in as well. How often have you sat in front of a beautiful card, pondering on which John, Henry or Margaret has sent it? And how about those where you can't even read the squiggle at the bottom? It's always those ones that have a smudged postmark, and I start to worry in case it's from someone we've forgotten to send a card to.

So if you can possibly make the time, put a little message into any cards you're sending today. It really is the loving messages and little bits of news which bring the best blessings to our house every December.

Your cue, I think, Sir Harry!

Bless This House

Bless this house, O Lord, we pray,
Make it safe by night and day;
Bless these walls, so firm and stout,
Keeping want and trouble out;
Bless the roof and chimneys tall,
Let Thy peace lie over all;
Bless this door, that it may prove
Ever open to joy and love.

Bless these windows shining bright,
Letting in God's heav'nly light;
Bless the hearth a-blazing there,
With smoke ascending like a prayer;
Bless the people here within,
Keep them pure and free from sin;
Bless us all that we may be
Fit, O Lord, to dwell with Thee.

Bless us all that one day we
May dwell, O Lord, with Thee.

Helen Taylor
(C. MCMXXVII as ''Bless the House'')
by Boosey & Co. Ltd, USA

DECEMBER 13

As Jesus and his disciples were on their way, he came to a village where a woman named Martha opened her home to him. She had a sister called Mary, who sat at the Lord's feet listening to what he said.

But Martha was distracted by all the preparations that had to be made. She came to him and asked, "Lord, don't you care that my sister has left me to do the work by myself? Tell her to help me!"

"Martha, Martha," the Lord answered, "you are worried and upset about many things, but only one thing is needed. Mary has chosen what is better, and it will not be taken away from her."

Luke 10:38–42 (NIV)

Bethlehem means "House of Bread". And one of the biggest parts of preparing for Christmas seems to be baking! Well, getting enough food in, anyway, and then preparing it for all the feasts! Even if you aren't having your family round, it's a time of year when people drop in unexpectedly, and it's nice to have a mince pie or a bit of Christmas cake to offer them. Even if you're on your own, you want to treat yourself to something a bit special in the depth of winter.

I've always thought Jesus was a bit hard on Martha, who had really been working her sox off to make nice things for him and the disciples to eat. I think he wanted to warn us about not spending too much time on elaborate preparations, when the important way to welcome people is with love.

But the Lord loved Martha just as much as Mary, so today let's be Martha-like, and bake a complicated Christmas cake, which is *delicious!*

(Before you begin, I'd better warn you – you need a lot of mixing bowls – and you'll probably be wishing Mary would help by washing up as you go along!)

Rich Christmas Cake

10oz/285g fine wholemeal flour
1 tsp salt
2 tsp ground cinnamon
1 tsp freshly grated nutmeg
½ tsp ground cloves

8oz unsalted butter
8oz/225g light brown sugar

4 large eggs (size 1 or 2)
2 tbsp honey

8oz/225g stoned muscatel raisins
8oz currants
4oz/110g chopped almonds
4oz glacé cherries, quartered
4oz mixed glacé fruit – chopped
2 tbsp finely chopped candied orange peel
1 tbsp finely grated orange peel zest

4 fl oz/120ml brandy or whisky

Preheat the oven to 150 C/300 F (gas mark 2).

And this is what you do:

Butter a round cake tin (8 inch or 20cm diameter and 3 inches high).

Line it with greaseproof paper.

Sift together flour, salt, cinnamon, nutmeg and cloves and set aside.

Cream the butter in a large bowl until it is pale and fluffy, then add the sugar.

Beat until the mixture is very light.

In another bowl, whisk the eggs with the honey, and beat this a little at a time into the butter and sugar mixture, adding a spoonful of the seasoned flour as you get near the end to prevent curdling.

In another bowl, combine the raisins, sultanas, currants, glacé cherries, glacé fruit, candied peel and nuts. Add a couple of spoonfuls of the seasoned flour, and mix.

Add the freshly grated zest of orange.

Mix very well.

Fold the remaining flour into the creamed mixture, followed by the fruit and nuts and finally the spirits.

Mix very thoroughly before turning the mixture into the prepared tin.

With the back of a spoon, make a shallow depression in the centre of the cake so that when the mixture has finished rising, the top will be about level.

Bake the cake in the cool oven for 1 hour before reducing the heat even lower to 140 C/275 F, gas mark 1 and baking for another 2 hours, or until a warm skewer plunged into the centre comes out cleanly.

Let the cake cool completely before taking it out of the tin and removing the greaseproof paper.

Store in an airtight container.

Go on! You can do it.

When Martha heard that Jesus was coming, she went out to meet him, but Mary stayed at home.

John 11:20 (NIV)

Oh, it's much easier to like Martha than Mary!

DECEMBER 14

At that time Mary got ready and hurried to a town in the hill country of Judah, where she entered Zacharias's home and greeted Elisabeth. When Elisabeth heard Mary's greeting, the baby leaped in her womb, and Elisabeth was filled with the Holy Spirit. In a loud voice she exclaimed: "Blessed are you among women, and blessed is the child you will bear! But why am I so favoured, that the mother of my Lord should come to me? As soon as the sound of your greeting reached my ears, the baby in my womb leaped for joy. Blessed is she who has believed that what the Lord has said to her will be accomplished!"

St Luke 1:39–45

And doesn't it make Christmas special if there's a new baby in the family? My Jan was born on December 14, and I'll never forget listening to the church bells on Christmas morning with my new baby in my arms. It was beautiful.

Then Jan's Daisy was born in America on December 13, but over here it was already December 14 because of the time difference, so when she telephoned from her hospital bed to say that Daisy had arrived safely, the first thing Scotty and I said to her was, "Happy birthday, darling!"

The only problem is that when these Christmas babies

grow up, they will keep on having birthdays 10 days before Christmas, and it makes life very difficult for their mother and grandmother!

Mary's song, the Magnificat, praising God for the gift to come, her baby, is said or sung every single evening of the year in all Anglican cathedrals, and every Sunday in the many churches where they still have Evensong. For some people Evensong is the most lovely of all services, and they try never to miss it. I remember sitting in Canterbury Cathedral one winter evening, up near where the choir sit, because there were only a few of us in the congregation that night, and realizing that the woman next to me was wearing her nightdress, dressing gown and slippers under her coat! She obviously lived near by and had got herself ready for bed before coming across for the service.

It made me think of our Neville. He used to come home from work and wash and change to go out, and on cold nights he'd always put his flannelette pyjama trousers on under his suit! It meant he could get into bed much quicker when he got home. Well, we didn't have anything like central heating in those days, and it was *very* cold in the north. And, oooh! – the sheets were so icy when you first got in!

For day fourteen, in gratitude for all the new babies that come into the world at Christmas time, let's turn up the words of the Magnificat in our bibles (it's St Luke's gospel, chapter 1, verses 46–55), or you could look at the hymn version, written by Bishop Timothy Dudley-Smith, which I've copied out here. Mary, preparing for the birth of her baby, was full of the hopes and dreams for a better world that every mother has when she thinks about the future of her children.

Magnificat

Tell out, my soul, the greatness of the Lord:
unnumbered blessings, give my spirit voice;
Tender to me the promise of his word;
in God my Saviour shall my heart rejoice.

Tell out, my soul, the greatness of his name:
make known his might, the deeds his arm has done;
His mercy sure, from age to age the same;
his holy name, the Lord, the Mighty One.

Tell out, my soul, the greatness of his might:
powers and dominions lay their glory by;
Proud hearts and stubborn wills are put to flight,
the hungry fed, the humble lifted high.

Tell out, my soul, the glories of his word:
firm is his promise, and his mercy sure.
Tell out, my soul, the greatness of the Lord
to children's children and for evermore.

By Timothy Dudley-Smith (b.1926)
based on St Luke 1:46–55 in
The New English Bible

O Come, O Come, Emmanuel

O come, O come, Emmanuel,
And ransom captive Israel,
That mourns in lonely exile here,
Until the Son of God appear.
    Rejoice! rejoice! Emmanuel
    Shall come to thee, O Israel.

O come, thou Rod of Jesse, free
Thine own from Satan's tyranny;
From depths of hell thy people save,
And give them victory o'er the grave.
    Rejoice! rejoice! Emmanuel
    Shall come to thee, O Israel.

O come, thou Dayspring, come and cheer
Our spirits by thine advent here;
Disperse the gloomy clouds of night,
And death's dark shadows put to flight.
    Rejoice! rejoice! Emmanuel
    Shall come to thee, O Israel.

O come, thou Key of David, come,
And open wide our heavenly home;
Make safe the way that leads on high,
And close the path to misery.
    Rejoice! rejoice! Emmanuel
    Shall come to thee, O Israel.

O come, O come, thou Lord of Might,
Who to thy tribes, on Sinai's height,
In ancient times didst give the law
In cloud and majesty and awe.
    Rejoice! rejoice! Emmanuel
    Shall come to thee, O Israel.

Latin c 13th century
tr. J. M. Neale (1919–66)

Do you know, it always gives me a bit of a tingle up
my spine, that Advent hymn. I suppose it's all those
imposing titles from the Old Testament: the Lord of
Might, the Key of David, the Dayspring, the Rod of
Jesse, Emmanuel – and all to describe a tiny baby!

It wakes you up, too. It's easy to get lulled into a
sentimental mood as Christmas gets closer, overspend-
ing on presents, but not really thinking about the great
gift God is giving – himself.

I remember when we were first told at Sunday School
about the Second Coming: Jesus coming again at the
end of time, not as a tiny baby, but as a judge. I was
very frightened, and hoped it wasn't going to happen
too soon! And when that Last Day comes, and we're
each standing in front of the Lord, it won't matter how
rich or powerful or clever we are. Only our deeds of
simple goodness are going to be of any use to us.

If you've ever feeling frightened by life, and wonder
what's going to become of us all, the words of Jesus in
the gospel of St John are very comforting:

"I have told you these things, so that in me you may have peace. In this world you will have trouble. But take heart! I have overcome the world."

The Holly and the Ivy

The holly and the ivy,
When they are both full grown,
Of all the trees that are in the wood,
The holly bears the crown:
The rising of the sun
And the running of the deer,
The playing of the merry organ,
Sweet singing in the choir.

The holly bears a blossom,
As white as the lily flower,
And Mary bore sweet Jesus Christ
To be our sweet Saviour:
The rising of the sun
And the running of the deer,
The playing of the merry organ,
Sweet singing in the choir.

The holly bears a berry,
As red as any blood,
And Mary bore sweet Jesus Christ
To do poor sinners good:
The rising of the sun
And the running of the deer,
The playing of the merry organ,
Sweet singing in the choir.

The holly bears a prickle,
As sharp as any thorn,
And Mary bore sweet Jesus Christ
On Christmas Day in the morn:
The rising of the sun
And the running of the deer,
The playing of the merry organ,
Sweet singing in the choir.

The holly bears a bark,
As bitter as any gall,
And Mary bore sweet Jesus Christ
For to redeem us all:
The rising of the sun
And the running of the deer,
The playing of the merry organ,
Sweet singing in the choir.

Traditional early 18th century

If you look up the meaning of the word "carol" in your dictionary – which you might guess I've just done – you'll find it means "a circle dance with a song". In medieval days this kind of dancing in a big ring would have been part of the ritual of village life on any of the major holy days, or on any really special day.

And even before that, in pre-Christian times, they would have had circle dances. In fact, I'm told that this carol, The Holly and the Ivy, probably was a pagan dance originally, with the men carrying holly and the girls carrying ivy, and the whole thing done, as a dancing and singing conversation between the lads and the lasses.

And it wasn't just an excuse for a bit of bawdy fun on a cold winter's day. They showed them the triumph of life over death, these evergreens, holly, ivy and mistletoe, still green and bearing berries and fruit when the rest of nature seemed dead. And what our pagan ancestors understood from nature, God's creation, we have now been shown even more clearly by Jesus himself.

So holly and ivy and mistletoe are still gathered from the woods and brought into the house in winter, just as they always have been. And that's what we'll do today. If you want to be really traditional, and salute your ancestors, you might even make them into a circle – a Christmas wreath for your front door!

DECEMBER 17

Only a week to go! Dear me, the older you get, the shorter the time seems to be between one Christmas and the next. I said to Scotty the other day that when we get really old, life will be all Christmas, with no time left in between at all!

Going into the West End of London in a taxi at Christmas time is really something! You see all the Christmas lights along the streets, in the shops, and hanging over the trees – because there are lots of trees growing in London – then there's the beautiful giant Christmas tree from Norway in Trafalgar Square; if you're lucky you might pass a Salvation Army band playing Christmas carols somewhere and collecting money off the shoppers hurrying past laden with exciting-looking packages. Last Christmas I said to Scotty, "Would you look – nearly every single person has got a bright green bag from M. and S. among their parcels!"

But when you get out of the taxi, and start to walk along the pavements, you become very conscious of the number of people huddled in doorways, or openly begging, "Excuse me. Have you got any change?" It's getting really awful. A lot of them look no older than our grandchildren, and I always worry and wonder about what their parents must be suffering, not knowing where their children are or what's happened to them.

At the Methodist Central Hall Westminster, The Revd Dr John Tudor (who is a particularly good friend of ours) and his team will be making preparations to give a Christmas lunch to hundreds of tramps and homeless people who will be turning up on Christmas Day. Hundreds of volunteers give up their own Christmas celebrations to help cook, serve and wash up a full Christmas lunch for people with no homes of their own.

I'll never forget going to a broadcast service at St Martin-in-the-Fields, in Trafalgar Square, and arriving early, so the service before was still finishing. I sat at the back in one of those box pews they have, and there were tramps sitting all round me in different pews, fast asleep and snoring loudly most of them! At the end the verger said, "Now the service is over, so you must all leave, please." They all got up and shuffled out, and there was one woman – I'd love to play her one day – she had two big bulging plastic bags with her, her whole life, and I watched her trudge out of one door, round the back, in through the next door, back into another pew, head down, and in two minutes she was fast asleep again!

While you're out shopping this Christmas, please spare a thought for people whose lives – even if it was their own fault – have got into a muddle they can't solve, leaving them with no home, no family, and in many cases, not a friend in the world.

Ballad of the Homeless Christ

A cry in the night
And a child is born;
A child in a stable,
There isn't any room:
A cry in the night, and God has made
Our homelessness his home.

A trial in the dark,
The disciples run;
They bring him to Pilate,
He stands there all alone:
A trial in the dark, and God has made
Our homelessness his home.

A man on a cross,
And the sun beats down;
Up there on the gallows
He's got a thorny crown:
A man on a cross, and God has made
Our homelessness his home.

A voice in the dawn
When the women came:
"You're looking for Jesus,
Don't seek him in a tomb":
A voice in the dawn, and God has made
Our homelessness his home.

Geoff Ainger (b. 1925)

DECEMBER 18

For many of my own, and older generations, the first half of this century, with two world wars, caused a lot of good people to lose their belief in a good God. And people stopped taking their children to church, too, or teaching them about the Christian religion. Christianity has been at the heart of our family life, and our national life, for so many centuries, but after the Second World War, fewer and fewer people were coming to church, or Sunday school.

The Lord never forces anyone, but he's always there, waiting for us, and I think people are beginning to look for him again. Many more young people are finding that saying their prayers and reading the Bible makes all the difference to their lives.

But while I have been preparing this little book, another war has been raging, in the Gulf. And we've practically been given ringside seats, watching the most terrible pictures on television day and night. By the time you are reading this, for most of us it will just be a memory. But there will be some families spending this Christmas without a son or a daughter, a father or a mother, a husband or a wife. It may be very hard for them to believe that God loves them.

So today in your prayers, please remember them.

I don't begin to understand the rights and wrongs of it all, do you? But I do know that only God can bring good out of our mistakes, and that this Christmas, like every Christmas, the angels still want to bring us their message of peace and love.

Still through the cloven skies they come,
With peaceful wings unfurled;
And still their heavenly music floats
O'er all the weary world;
Above its sad and lowly plains
They bend on hovering wing;
And ever o'er its Babel sounds
The blessed angels sing.

Yet with the woes of sin and strife
The world has suffered long;
Beneath the angel-strain have rolled
Two thousand years of wrong;
And man, at war with man, hears not
The love-song which they bring:
O hush the noise, ye men of strife,
And hear the angels sing!

From "It Came Upon a Midnight Clear"
Edmund Sears (1810–76)

DECEMBER 19

In the fore-court, lit by the dim rays of a horn lantern, some eight or ten little field mice stood in a semi-circle, red worsted comforters round their throats, their fore-paws thrust deep into their pockets, their feet jiggling for warmth. With bright beady eyes they glanced shyly at each other, sniggering a little, sniffing and applying coat-sleeves a good deal. As the door opened, one of the elder ones that carried the lantern was just saying, "Now then, one, two, three!" and forthwith their shrill little voices uprose on the air, singing one of the old-time carols that their fore-fathers composed in fields that were fallow and held by frost, or when snowbound in chimney corners, and handed down to be sung in the miry street of lamp-lit windows at Yuletime.

Kenneth Graham
extract from *The Wind in the Willows* (Methuen)

And it is just like that, isn't it, when you hear a knock on the door, and there in the porch you find a small group of carol singers, huddled together round their dim lantern, heads bent over their books. If they sing Good King Wenceslas, you can bet the men will all boom out the part of the King very lustily, but the children and women will only just be heard, nervously singing the part of the Page. It's always the same. I do love 'em!

I think I mentioned in my *Praise Be!* Yearbook how, during the years when Jan was living in Beverly Hills, we used to put the telephone receiver out of the window when our local church carol singers visited the Mews, and they would end by shouting, "Happy Christmas, Jan!"

If you haven't heard any carol singers for some years, why don't you telephone your local church (the number will be in the book!) and tell them that you and your neighbours would welcome them. Only you must be prepared to give them some hospitality. It gets very cold out there on a December night.

There are always lots of charity carol concerts at this time of year. We always try to get to "The King of Carol Concerts" at the Dome, in Brighton, run every year by our friend Peter Shilling, a Methodist Minister. It's marvellous, the huge circular hall of the dome is always packed, and Peter invites local "celebrities" onto the platform to do their party pieces, and we all sing lots of carols and raise thousands of pounds for various good causes.

One of the occasions I especially enjoy in London is the Salvation Army's annual Carolcade in their Oxford Street citadel, with a great band and hundreds of uniformed Salvation Army officers all singing their hearts out. The money they collect goes to support their work on the streets of London with down-and-outs and homeless people. What a wonderful band of Christians they are. (One year Princess Diana came along, and I had the honour of being presented to her. Talking to her was just as easy and natural as, well, talking to any of you!)

So my suggestion for December 19 – or for one of the days before Christmas – is this: don't stay in every

evening watching television – unless I'm on. (No, I
don't mean it!) Please do go out to one of the charity
carol concerts you'll find organized in every city, town
and village at this time of year, and as well as having
a really good sing, you'll be helping a good cause. Or
ring up your local church and say that you and your
neighbours would love to hear some carols, and would
provide a hot drink and a donation if a group of carol
singers wanted to come your way with their lanterns.

Better still – put on some warm clothes and go out
carol singing yourself!

DECEMBER 20

Clear away! There was nothing they wouldn't have cleared away, or couldn't have cleared away, with old Fezziwig looking on. It was done in a minute. Every movable was packed off, as if it were dismissed from public life for evermore; the floor was swept and watered, the lamps were trimmed, fuel was heaped upon the fire; and the warehouse was as snug, and warm, and dry, and bright a ball-room, as you would desire to see upon a winter's night.

In came a fiddler with a music-book, and went up to the lofty desk, and made an orchestra of it, and tuned like fifty stomach-aches. In came Mrs Fezziwig, one vast substantial smile. In came the three Miss Fezziwigs, beaming and loveable. In came the six young followers whose hearts they broke. In came all the young men and women employed in the business. In came the housemaid, with her cousin, the baker. In came the cook, with her brother's particular friend, the milkman. In came the boy from over the way, who was suspected of not having board enough from his master. . .

In they all came, one after another; some shyly, some boldly, some gracefully, some awkwardly, some pushing, some pulling; in they all came, anyhow and everyhow. . .

There were dances, and there were forfeits, and more dances, and there was cake, and there was negus, and there was a great piece of Cold Roast, and there was a great piece of Cold Boiled, and there were mince-pies, and plenty of beer. . .

When the clock struck eleven, this domestic ball broke up. Mr and Mrs Fezziwig took their stations, one on either side the door, and shaking hands with every person individually as he or she went out, wished him or her a Merry Christmas.

From *A Christmas Carol*
Charles Dickens (1812–70)

If only all office parties were as warm and loving as the Fezziwigs'! Nevertheless, I want to write a word for the many people who are not Christians but who do want to celebrate Christmas. Even non-believers are stirred up with deep feelings of hope at this time of year. And its not just wanting to eat and drink too much and all those commercial things. They like giving loving presents to their families and spending time with them.

I think a lot of it has to do with memories. Memories of childhood, and the days when we still believed in Father Christmas, and expectantly hung out a stocking at the end of the bed. And memories of stories, like Charles Dickens' *A Christmas Carol*, with episodes like the Fezziwigs' Christmas party, that are so well described, you almost feel you were there. And things we've heard on the radio – oh! those days spent sitting on a big horsehair-stuffed sofa, listening to John Masefield's Box of Delights on Children's Hour. And the things we ate. I always remember my father coming home in triumph on Christmas Eve with – stand back – a fresh pineapple! And he always brought a box of tangerines, each one half wrapped in silver paper. My mother always bought dates and figs and crystallized ginger. Splendiferous!

And where's the harm, if these memories make us feel we want to be a bit kinder to our fellow men? In spite of all the glitter, I think many non-believers do get a glimpse of God's love gathering them in – even if they soon forget it again.

But why am I trying to explain what I mean, when it's already been done so well in verse by Sir John Betjeman? Let's make that our task for December 20 – to read his poem called Christmas. (By the by, do you remember George Cole, in his "Arthur Daley" voice, reading this on television one Christmas? He did it so well.)

Christmas

The bells of waiting Advent ring,
The Tortoise stove is lit again
And lamp-oil light across the night
Has caught the streaks of winter rain
In many a stained-glass window sheen
From Crimson Lake to Hooker's Green.

The holly in the windy hedge
And round the Manor House the yew
Will soon be stripped to deck the ledge,
The altar, font and arch and pew,
So that the villagers can say
"The church looks nice" on Christmas Day.

Provincial public houses blaze
And Corporation tramcars clang,

On lighted tenements I gaze
Where paper decorations hang,
And bunting in the red Town Hall
Says "Merry Christmas to you all."

And London shops on Christmas Eve
Are strung with silver bells and flowers
As hurrying clerks the City leave
To pigeon-haunted classic towers,
And marbled clouds go scudding by
The many-steepled London sky.

And girls in slacks remember Dad,
And oafish louts remember Mum,
And sleepless children's hearts are glad,
And Christmas-morning bells say "Come!"
Even to shining ones who dwell
Safe in the Dorchester Hotel.

And is it true? And is it true,
This most tremendous tale of all,
Seen in a stained-glass window's hue,
A Baby in an ox's stall?
The Maker of the stars and sea
Become a Child on earth for me?

And is it true? For if it is,
No loving fingers tying strings
Around those tissued fripperies,
The sweet and silly Christmas things,
Bath salts and inexpensive scent
And hideous tie so kindly meant.

No love that in a family dwells,
No carolling in frosty air,
Nor all the steeple-shaking bells

Can with this single Truth compare –
That God was Man in Palestine
And lives to-day in Bread and Wine.

Sir John Betjeman (1906–84)

DECEMBER 21

After the longest day, the 21st of June, until the 21st of December, the days grow shorter and the nights longer. Brrr! I wish we could all hibernate sometimes, on a cold, dank December afternoon, when it's dark by three o'clock.

Our forefathers, the ancient Britons, used to think that the sun was dying, and would perhaps go out altogether, leaving them to struggle in the cold darkness.

As the days gradually began to stretch out again after 21 December, those ancestors of ours lit roaring fires, made merry with songs and dancing, and gave thanks and praise for the return to life of the sun.

Then the first Christians arrived, and told them that they were quite right to celebrate, because an even greater light than the sun had come to life in the dark world. A baby had been born, bringing such a light that he had shown everyone everywhere, whether simple or wise, that at the heart of the universe lies the love of God. So the ancient, pagan celebration of the mid-December sun became Christmas, the celebration of the birthday of the son of God.

Here's a poem you might like to read, by G. K. Chesterton. It's just the thing for a cold, dark, 21 December afternoon.

A Child of the Snows

There is heard a hymn when the panes are dim,
And never before or again,
When the nights are strong with a darkness long,
And the dark is alive with the rain.

Never we know but in sleet and in snow,
The place where the great fires are,
That the mist of the earth is a raging mirth
And the heart of the earth is a star.

And at night we win to the ancient inn
Where the child in the frost is furled,
We follow the feet where all souls meet
At the inn at the end of the world.

The gods lie dead where the leaves lie red,
For the flame of the sun is flown,
The gods lie cold where the leaves lie gold,
And a child comes forth alone.

G. K. Chesterton (1874–1936)

Whatever the weather, let's praise the Lord for the return of the sun each December 21, which showed our ancestors that the world isn't going to grow darker and colder for ever. And the baby in the manger at Bethlehem, the beginning and centre of all life, will show us, sure as sunrise, the way to another spring.

DECEMBER 22

Do you have a little crib, like a model of the nativity scene, which you bring out in December? People usually put out the stable first (or a painted, three-sided cardboard box!) with perhaps just one lonely ox in it. Then nearer to Christmas day, they put in the figures of Mary and Joseph, and a donkey. On Christmas Day, or at midnight on Christmas Eve, they put the baby Jesus into the manger. Then they add two shepherds and a little lamb, and, on a different shelf, three wise men and a camel (still on their way, you see).

Many churches hold a special Crib Service. A different child brings in each of the figures, one at a time, and places them in the stable, while the vicar tells the story of who came to Bethlehem and why and how, and everyone sings the story in carols.

I was looking out of the window last December, during a very cold spell, and I saw something on the path that I thought was a bird, then I thought it was a leaf. Then I thought, no, it is a bird, and then I thought, no, it is a leaf. The more I looked at it, the more I couldn't decide whether it was a bird or a leaf, so in the end I put on my coat and hat and furry boots and went outside to investigate.

It was a bird, a little sparrow, with his feathers all puffed out to keep him warm, but something was the matter, because I was able to walk right up to him, bend down and pick him up, and he didn't move. He was alive, because he looked at me with a pair of bright eyes, but he didn't struggle in my hands.

I looked him over to see if he was injured, but he didn't seem to be. I carried him carefully indoors, holding him very gently, thinking I would find a little box to put him in. But I was wondering what I was going to do with him after that, because, to be honest, I couldn't see Scotty and me spending Christmas going in and out to dig for worms in the garden, and I didn't know what the local vet would say if I brought him a little sparrow to look after!

I said a little prayer. I think I said, "Lord, your holy spirit flies over the face of all the earth. If it is possible, let this little sparrow fly again, too."

And the little bird started to struggle. I carried him to the front door, opened my hands, and away he flew as though nothing had ever been the matter with him.

No, I don't say it was a miracle. I expect that he had been suffering from hypothermia, and the warmth of my hands and the house revived him. But it was such a happy thing to happen a few days before Christmas, and like all good things, a gift from the Lord – for which I was very grateful.

I wonder if you've come across this poem by Rudyard Kipling.

Eddi's Service

Eddi, priest of St Wilfrid
In the chapel at Manhood End,

Ordered a midnight service
For such as cared to attend.

But the Saxons were keeping Christmas,
And the night was stormy as well.
Nobody came to service
Though Eddi rang the bell.

"Wicked weather for walking,"
Said Eddi of Manhood End.
"But I must go on with the service
For such as care to attend."

The altar candles were lighted, –
An old marsh donkey came,
Bold as a guest invited,
And stared at the guttering flame.

The storm beat on at the windows,
The water splashed on the floor,
And a wet yoke-weary bullock
Pushed in through the open door.

"How do I know what is greatest,
How do I know what is least?
That is My Father's business,"
Said Eddi, Wilfrid's priest.

"But, three are gathered together –
Listen to me and attend,
I bring good news, my brethren!"
Said Eddi, of Manhood End.

And he told the Ox of a manger
And a stall in Bethlehem,
And he spoke to the Ass of a Rider
That rode to Jerusalem.

They steamed and dripped in the chancel,
They listened and never stirred,
While, just as though they were Bishops,
Eddi preached them The Word.

Till the gale blew off on the marshes
And the windows showed the day,
And the Ox and the Ass together
Wheeled and clattered away.

And when the Saxons mocked him.
Said Eddi of Manhood End,
"I dare not shut His chapel
On such as care to attend."

Rudyard Kipling (1865–1936)
in *Rewards and Fairies*

December 23

Last Christmas I played the part of old Mrs Clarke in the television series *All Creatures Great and Small*. Oh, I enjoyed playing Mrs Clarke, an interesting woman she was, still open to learning about life, even though an old lady. She had lost her son in the war, when he was fighting in Italy. (You probably realize that the series is all set in Yorkshire in the years just after the Second World War – a time and a place Scotty and I remember so well. And don't you love all those beautiful vintage cars they drive around in?)

Anyway, the indomitable Mrs Clarke runs a farm all on her own, up in the Yorkshire dales, and she is very independent-minded and proud.

The first time I played her, the Christmas before last, the story was about an Italian ex-prisoner-of-war who had stayed on in England, and had come to work for the farmer next door to Mrs Clarke, as a shepherd. In that episode, she had to learn to "love thy neighbour" – even though he was one of "the enemy" who had killed her only son. And she did.

Last Christmas the story had moved on, and Mrs Clarke was beginning to feel her years. She kept having accidents, but she didn't want to accept help from anyone. You saw her carrying heavy buckets of water out to her animals, walking with a stick.

It's not easy for proud old people to accept help, but sometimes being too independent can be a form of selfishness. Last Christmas Mrs Clarke had to discover that when she accepted help from the people who loved her, she was really giving them something, too.

Scotty always helps me learn my scripts – we get up early in the mornings, and he gives me my cues and prompts me, so in the end he often knows my words almost as well as I do. We both enjoyed learning "Mrs Clarke" very much, and thought there was a lesson in it for all of us. So on December 23, let's learn the grace to receive, as well as to give.

On December 23 I always enjoy going along to church for the service of carols and readings, and hearing again the old familiar words:

And there were in the same country shepherds abiding in the field, keeping watch over their flock by night.

And, lo, the angel of the Lord came upon them, and the glory of the Lord shone round about them: and they were sore afraid.

And the angel said unto them. "Fear not: for, behold, I bring you good tidings of great joy, which shall be to all people.

"For unto you is born this day in the city of David, a Saviour, which is Christ the Lord.

"And this shall be a sign unto you; Ye shall find the babe wrapped in swaddling clothes, lying in a manger."

St Luke 2:8–12 (AV)

CHRISTMAS EVE

Even though Scotty and I sometimes have to miss the local service of lessons and carols on December 23, we try *never* to miss the one broadcast from King's College chapel, Cambridge, on Christmas Eve. Did you know that the BBC have been broadcasting the service of Nine Lessons and Carols from the King's College Chapel every year since 1928, with only one exception, in 1930? The service was devised in 1918 by Eric Milner-White, as "a gift to the townspeople of Cambridge". And now it's become a gift for countless families all over the country – and all over the world. It goes out every Christmas Eve on the BBC World Service as well as Radio 4, so when you are listening to it, you are linked up to people in such far away places as India and Egypt. In the war years it was still broadcast, but without it being announced where it was coming from – for security reasons. The sound of the beautiful singing in that wonderful acoustic is so distinctive, I don't suppose they fooled anyone!

I like to listen to it while we are "dressing the tree" – which we always do on Christmas Eve – never before. Daisy and I did it together last year, because we all spent Christmas at Jan's, and had a big tree in the same room in which I present *Praise Be!* in the Spring.

I always think "Now it's really Christmas!" when I hear it beginning, as it always does, with a young boy chorister singing the first verse of Once in Royal David's City all on his own. I think he must stand a long way from the microphone, and the huge acoustic of the chapel makes it sound like the distant voice of a young angel from heaven and that's exactly what it sounded like to me when I heard my granddaughter singing that same first verse from somewhere outside the hall at a carol concert at Benenden School, where she was a pupil. She was fifteen at the time. Oh dear, the tears wouldn't keep back! It was beautiful!

Once in Royal David's City

Once in Royal David's city
Stood a lowly cattle-shed,
Where a mother laid her Baby,
In a manger for His bed:
Mary was that mother mild,
Jesus Christ her little child.

He came down to earth from heaven
Who is God and Lord of all,
And His shelter was a stable,
And His cradle was a stall;
With the poor and mean and lowly
Lived on earth our Saviour holy.

And through all His wondrous childhood
He would honour and obey,
Love, and watch the lowly maiden
In whose gentle arms he lay.
Christian children all must be
Mild, obedient, good as He.

For He is our childhood's pattern:
Day by day like us He grew;

He was little, weak and helpless;
Tears and smiles like us He knew;
And He feeleth for our sadness,
And He shareth in our gladness.

And our eyes at last shall see Him,
Though His own redeeming love,
For that Child, so dear and gentle
Is our Lord in heaven above;
And He leads His children on
To the place where He is gone.

Not in that poor lowly stable,
With the oxen standing by,
We shall see Him, but in heaven,
Set at God's right hand on high;
Where like stars His children crowned
All in white shall wait around.

Mrs C. F. Alexander (1818–95)

Late at night on Christmas Eve, when the last parcel is wrapped, supper things cleared away, children all in bed, then go by yourself into the room where you have decorated the Christmas tree. Turn out all the lights except the ones on the tree and drink in the smell of pine forest, the silence, and the sheer sparkling beauty of the thing.

You may even be moved to sing a little carol softly to yourself. . .

Silent Night

Silent night, holy night!
All is calm, all is bright
Round yon virgin mother and child.
Holy infant, so tender and mild,
Sleep in heavenly peace,
Sleep in heavenly peace.

Silent night, holy night!
Shepherds quake at the sight:
Glories stream from heaven afar,
Heavenly hosts sing: Alleluia,
Christ the Saviour is born!
Christ the Saviour is born!

Silent night, holy night!
Son of God, love's pure light,
Radiance beams from thy holy face
With the dawn of redeeming grace,
Jesus, Lord, at thy birth,
Jesus, Lord, at thy birth.

Joseph Mohr (1702–1883)
English translation Anon

And then it's time for Midnight Mass. In our village people arrive from all directions, some in cars, some walking along with torches, some yawning, some, let's be honest, a bit tiddly from an evening in the pub, but everybody very happy to be coming together to celebrate Christmas. It almost seems like a re-enactment of the very first Christmas, with shepherds crowding into the tiny stable to get a glimpse of the baby, full of awe, if only half understanding why they were there.

And suddenly there was with the angel a multitude of the heavenly host praising God, and saying,
"Glory to God in the highest, and on earth peace, good will toward men."

St Luke 2:13–14 (AV)

CHRISTMAS DAY

Christmas morning always began the same way when I was a child – with the Salvation Army Band arriving in the middle of Cheapside and playing "Christians Awake!" And if there were any Christians who weren't already awake, they soon were!

The words of this carol were written by John Byrom – another Lancastrian – as a Christmas present for his daughter, Dolly. On Christmas morning 1749 Dolly found the words on a sheet of paper headed "Christmas Day. For Dolly." And a year later, on Christmas morning 1750, the Byrom family were all woken up by the choir of Stockport Parish Church singing "Christians Awake!" beneath their windows, to the tune "Yorkshire", which John Wainwright, their local church organist, had especially composed for it.

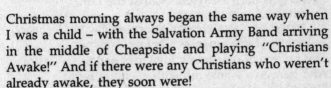

Christians Awake!
Salute the Happy Morn

Christians, awake, salute the happy morn
Whereon the Saviour of the world was born;
Rise to adore the mystery of love,
Which hosts of angels chanted from above;
With them the joyful tidings first begun
Of God Incarnate and the Virgin's Son:

Then to the watchful shepherds it was told,
Who heard the angelic herald's voice, "Behold,
I bring good tidings of a Saviour's birth
To you and all the nations upon earth;
This day hath God fulfilled His promised word,
This day is born a Saviour, Christ the Lord."

He spake; and straightway the celestial choir,
In hymns of joy, unknown before, conspire:
The praises of redeeming love they sang,
And heaven's whole orb with alleluyas rang:
God's highest glory was their anthem still,
Peace upon earth, and unto men goodwill.

To Bethlehem straight the enlightened shepherds ran
To see the wonder God had wrought for man,
And found, with Joseph and the blessed Maid,
Her Son, the Saviour, in a manger laid;
Then to their flocks, still praising God, return,
And their glad hearts with holy rapture burn.

O may we keep and ponder in our mind
God's wondrous love in saving lost mankind;
Trace we the Babe, who hath retrieved our loss,
From His poor manger to His bitter cross;
Tread in His steps, assisted by His grace,
Till man's first heavenly state again takes place.

Then may we hope, the angelic hosts among,
To sing, redeemed, a glad triumphal song.
He that was born upon this joyful day
Around us all His glory shall display;
Saved by His love, incessant we shall sing
Eternal praise to heaven's almighty King.

John Byrom (1692–1763)

Our "Sally Ann" also used to play and sing "While shepherds watched their flocks by night", to the tune Lyngham, which on *Songs of Praise* is usually sung to the words "O for a Thousand Tongues to Sing". I keep hoping that one year they'll have Lyngham to "While shepherds watched" – just once, just for me!

I thought Jan and William had gone daft last Christmas! Well, they gave Scotty and me so many parcels. There were all sorts of lovely things, and one great idea they'd had, was to give us a beautiful selection of complete meals, deep frozen, so we can keep them in the cottage freezer and not have to keep bringing stuff down from London. It was a very thoughtful present – the only thing is, we noticed that all the meals were for four people, so now, whenever Scotty and I get one out, Jan and William are invited round to share it with us. Not so daft, my daughter!

After we'd opened some of the parcels, we all had to go outside to watch Jan perform a graceful circuit on her new bicycle. James and Daisy were both home for Christmas, so it was all very joyous.

Everyone enjoys going to church at Christmas time. Our village church is always full, both at the Midnight Mass on Christmas Eve and the ten o'clock Family Service on Christmas morning.

Even if you are not a churchgoer yourself, or haven't been to church for years, come along this Christmas, and see how loving and happy it is. You'll find the place full, and you certainly won't be the only one if you can't find your place in the book – there's me for a start! But you'll go home and enjoy Christmas Day with a much lighter heart.

Don't worry about not being sure whether or not you believe in God. He knows about that tiny corner in your heart that wants to believe, and if you just go and wish him a Happy Birthday, that'll be good enough for him.

Good Enough for Him

Jesus was born in a stable:
There was no room in the inn.
He had a stall for a cradle;
That was good enough for him.

Cattle asleep in the corner,
Joseph kept watch from within.
Can you imagine the sorrow?
That was good enough for him.

No kingly robes for his vesture,
No royal hall for this One.
But Mary fondled her treasure,
For He was God's dear Son.

Jesus was born in a stable:
There was no room in the inn.
He had a stall for a cradle;
That was good enough for him.

Peter Chesters (1960)

BOXING DAY

I always think it's rather a wonderful day, Boxing Day. In London a traditional thing is to go out for a walk in the park today, wearing your new Christmas clothes. Men who all year have only been seen early in the mornings, hurrying off to work in dark suits, and whom you can hardly imagine without a briefcase in their hand, will appear in the parks on Boxing Day wearing lovingly hand-knitted blue and red and green pullovers, with a pattern round the chest. And they are accompanied by wives and children, also wearing beautifully knitted hats, gloves and scarves, clothes quite unlike the ones anybody wears on any other day of the year! I always enjoy the Boxing Day parade.

If it's cold and frosty or snowy, everyone puts their new knitted gloves and scarves along the radiators when they get back indoors. You know, that's something I always associate with the days after Christmas? The smell of damp new wool steaming gently along the radiators!

The days after Christmas are a good time for calling on friends and neighbours. Round our way it's become quite a custom when lots of guests are invited for lunch, for each of them to provide a different course. Someone brings a starter, several people might bring different puddings, someone provides vegetables or a salad, someone else brings a fish course, others might bring some wine or a fruit cup.

It's nice, because it means that the hosts can look

forward to seeing family and friends without having to slave all morning to provide all the food. And it's always a wonderful meal, because everyone competes to bring the nicest dish!

If you want to try this, and want to provide a course to take to friends, but can't think what to do, here's a suggestion that will make you a star attraction. And all you have to do is make some soup! (The only drawback is, you really needed to have begun preparations for this soup last February or March, by buying some pumpkin seeds, because it's best if you've grown them yourself!)

But nobody has yet come up with an idea more startling, satisfying or simple than Jan's Pumpkin Soup!

William, Jan's husband says growing pumpkins is very easy. In fact he says the problem is not growing them, but preventing them from taking over the whole world! What you do need is a garden or an alloment with enough space for a compost heap – because on the compost heap is where your pumpkins will grow.

First you buy your packet of seeds in February, and plant them in little pots or in a tray on the kitchen windowsill. When all danger of frost is past, in May or June, you stick the healthiest seedlings out round the compost heap. But believe me, you're only going to need one plant, so don't plant out too many of them.

After that all you have to do is to keep them from drying out, which can be a problem in times of drought. I remember seeing Jan going to and fro with buckets of washing-up and bath water to pour over hers one summer. But usually in England we get plenty of rain. In America they grow the pumpkins alongside the corn, so the corn grows on the dry top layers of soil, and the pumpkins grow underneath in the cool moisture of the trenches between the rows.

Pumpkins grow very quickly – in fact they're a bit outer space! – so they are interesting for children to watch. Every two or three days big new leaves unfold. Once three or four small pumpkins have appeared on the plant, William pinches out the end, or it will go on growing to produce thirty or forty pumpkins.

They will be big and ripe and ready to eat by October or November, but they can be stored wonderfully well in a garage, shed or barn until Christmas.

Pumpkin Soup

Serves 6
4oz/110g butter
1 tbsp sunflower oil
1 onion finely chopped
1 tsp ground coriander
1 tsp ground cumin
8oz/225g pumpkin in chunks
8oz celery in chunks
1 pt hot chicken stock
salt and pepper
8oz tomatoes (skinned and chopped)
    (or an 8oz tin of tomatoes is just as good.)
for the garnish:
    3 tbsp chopped parsley.

Heat half the butter and all the oil in a saucepan.

Cook the onion in the butter and oil until gold and transparent, not brown or burnt.

Add the spices, and cook for 2–3 minutes, stirring.

Add the pumpkin and celery and cook over a gentle heat for 4–5 minutes, stirring.

Add the chicken stock, bring to the boil, then put the lid of the saucepan almost on and simmer for 25 minutes.

Season with the salt and pepper.

Meanwhile!:

Melt the remaining butter in a small frying pan and cook the tomatoes for 4 minutes, until they are soft (if you are using tinned tomatoes, you just need to heat them up a little).

Add the tomatoes to the soup.

Allow to cool slightly, then puree the soup briefly in a food processor, stopping before it becomes totally smooth. If you haven't got a blender, you can push it through a sieve.

All this can be done a day or two in advance, because the flavour just gets better and better.

Then you take the scooped out pumpkin shell – or use a second pumpkin scooped out enough to hold all the soup – and warm it in the oven.

Reheat the soup, and pour it into the warmed pumpkin shell, sprinkling it with finely chopped parsley.

The piece you have cut out of the top of the pumpkin, with its stalk still on – of course fits perfectly as a lid. In fact, I was quite bamboozled at Jan's. I thought, "What's the pumpkin on the table for?"

If you're going to take it to someone else's home, put the hot soup in a Thermos, and the garnish and pumpkin shell and lid in a separate bag, but remember to warm them up before pouring the soup in. The soup is golden in colour and warm in flavour, and serving it in a pumpkin shell causes a sensation!

It's so rare for there to be time to write letters, but between Christmas and the New Year, unless of course I'm rehearsing, there are these wonderfully peaceful, unbusy days, and there's plenty of time for letter-writing. And for visiting friends in hospital.

Shortly after Christmas last year I had to go into St Mary's Hospital, Paddington, for a heart by-pass operation, and hundreds of people I've never even met sent me such kind cards, letters and flowers while I was there. You cannot know how much that meant to me. Many of them didn't put an address or even their surname, and I couldn't have replied to them all anyway, because there were so many. And I know they didn't expect me to, because they were just being loving. If you were one of those kind people, I do thank you from the bottom of my heart.

Someone gave me a little book called "God is . . .", and the one I like best is "God is . . . the greatest ever Heart Surgeon!"

As I lay in hospital I sometimes had strange dreams, but each time I woke up and saw all the flowers and cards, I knew that the Lord wasn't far away.

How Far Is It to Bethlehem?

How far is it to Bethlehem?
Not very far.
Shall we find the stable-room
Lit by a star?

Can we see the little child,
Is He within?

If we lift the wooden latch,
May we go in?

May we stroke the creatures there –
Ox, ass, or sheep?
May we peep like them and see
Jesus asleep?

If we touch His tiny hand,
Will He awake?
Will He know we've come so far
Just for His sake?

Great kings have precious gifts,
And we have naught?
Little smiles and little tears
Are all we brought.

For all weary children
Mary must weep;
Here, on His bed of straw
Sleep, children, sleep.

God, in his mother's arms,
Babes in the byre,
Sleep, as they sleep who find
Their heart's desire.

Frances Chesterton
(wife of G. K. Chesterton)
(in *The Golden Staircase* – Nelson)

EPIPHANY

Twelve days have gone by since Christmas morning. The evenings close in a little later each day on our cottage in Jan's winter garden. The hard brown earth is broken by green daffodil shoots, and soon early snowdrops and crocuses will be in flower among the frosty blades of grass, and even they will be beaten by bright yellow aconites, always the first in our garden to herald the New Year.

> Arise, shine; for thy light is come, and the glory of the Lord is risen upon thee.
>
> Isaiah 60:1 (AV)

If you go to your church to celebrate the Epiphany, you will hear and sing about a light that shines in the darkness, because Jesus is in the world. It's the time of the three wise men from the east following a star to the stable in Bethlehem, and taking the news of what they found to men and women all over the world, so that now the story has been handed down to us.

This is the time of bright hope.

So, in the famous words of Tiny Tim in *A Christmas Carol*:

"God bless us, every one."

Acknowledgements

'Good Enough for Him' by Peter Chesters © 1960 Josef Weinberger Ltd, reproduced by permission of the copyright owners. 'The Ballad of the Homeless Christ' by Geoffrey Ainger, reproduced by permission of Stainer & Bell Ltd, London, England. 'Tell out, my soul' © Timothy Dudley-Smith, reproduced by permission of the author. 'Christmas' by John Betjeman, reproduced by permission of John Murray Ltd. 'The Christingle Song' from *New Songs of Praise 5*, 1990 reproduced by permission of Oxford University Press.